AN UNOFFICIAL GRAPHIC NOVEL
FOR MINECRAFTERS

CHASING HEROBRINE

CARA J. STEVENS

ART BY **DAVID NORGREN**
AND **ELIAS NORGREN**

SCHOLASTIC INC.

Special thanks to Cara J. Stevens, David Norgren, and Elias Norgren

No part of this publication may be reproduced, stored in a retrieval system, or
transmitted in any form or by any means, electronic, mechanical, photocopying,
recording, or otherwise, without written permission of the publisher. For information
regarding permission, write to Sky Pony Press, an imprint of Skyhorse Publishing,
Inc., 307 West 36th Street, 11th Floor, New York, NY 10018.

ISBN 978-1-338-20860-3

The publisher does not have any control over and does not assume any responsibility
for author or third-party websites or their content.

12 11 10 9 8 7 6 5 4 3 2   17 18 19 20 21 22

Printed in the U.S.A.   40

First Scholastic printing, September 2017

Cover design by Brian Peterson
Cover illustration by David Norgren
Designer: Joshua Barnaby

INTRODUCTION

If you have played Minecraft, then you know all about Minecraft worlds. They're made of blocks you can mine: coal, dirt, and sand. In the game, you'll find many different creatures, lands, and villages inhabited by strange villagers with bald heads. The villagers who live there have their own special, magical worlds that are protected by a string of border worlds to stop outsiders from finding them.

When we last left off in the small border world of Xenos, Phoenix, T.H., and Xander had just conquered the Ender Dragon and reclaimed the legendary Dragon Scrolls, only to return and find Phoenix is no longer welcome within the gates of her own village.

She and her family have settled into their new home outside the village, along with a growing number of supporters. Their small town has expanded to include a farm, some stores, and even a small school.

Our story resumes on Halloween, as Phoenix and her friends are getting ready for a night of fun and a touch of mischief. But none of them are prepared for the real-life ghost story they are about to encounter that may make this Halloween celebration their last...

CHAPTER 1

ALL HALLOWS' EVE

I'm okay. It's going to be okay.

Let's start with this house.

CLICK!

Trick...

...or...

...treat!

Oh, what cute costumes. Aren't you just darlings? Have some apples!

Another apple. Why can't people be more imaginative?

Yay! I got an apple!

Welcome, children!

Hi, Ole Baba...I mean, Bailey! Hi, Leila!

You look so beautiful like that, Leila!

I wanted to dress like a good witch for once. No more evil witch for me!

Our new little village is shaping up nicely, isn't it? How do you like living here, kids?

It's nice having Phoenix back home with us, even if we did have to leave the safety of Xenos and the library.

Do you miss it?

Nah. I feel safe now that things are back to normal.

Maybe now you can stop sleeping on my floor and sleep in your own room.

Poor Xander is still afraid of things that go bump in the night.

Take a cookie! I baked them myself!

These are delicious!

Where are you kids off to tonight?

Phoenix and Xander's parents are having a big party in the barn. You should come!

I love parties! I haven't been to one since before I was turned into a witch.

I haven't been to a party since you left home either. I'm so glad you're back.

I'm glad I'm not a zombie anymore, thanks to Phoenix and T.H.

Leila! Bailey! So glad you could make it.

And you kids-- you should have been here an hour ago. I was getting worried.

Were you trick-or-treating all this time?

Welllll...Not the WHOLE time...

Who's that bozo?

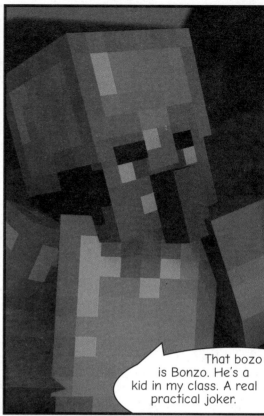

That bozo is Bonzo. He's a kid in my class. A real practical joker.

Think he was the one who did it?

Nah. He looked too scared.

He's more of a storyteller. Mostly harmless. He doesn't grief kids.

We should question him anyway, just to be sure.

First, we need to clean up the mess.

Sure thing, Mom.

I'm going to see what Bonzo knows about all this.

Hi. I'm Phoenix.

I know. I'm Bonzo.

I know...

What I don't know is what part you had in all this.

Nothing! Honest! The little squirts just wanted a good scary story.

I believe him.

I do, too. You looked pretty scared when the lights went on!

Surprised, not scared. There's a difference.

As long as you're here, wanna help clean up?

Um, I think I hear my mom calling me. Sorry.

I don't think his mom was calling him.

CHAPTER 2

THE MARK OF HERBIE

Never mind.
What's going on?
I don't know. I heard a scream.
Us, too.
Whose house is this?
I dunno. Someone who just moved here from Xenos. It wasn't here last week.

Hey, a little help up here?

It's Bonzo!

What happened?

Thanks for the rescue!

I was asleep in my bed and I heard rushing water.

Then, my bed started floating. There was water everywhere! I heard a creepy voice but didn't see anyone.

Then my bed floated up the stairs, out the roof hatch, and I was stuck on the roof!

So that was you screaming?

I yelled in surprise.

You dared to summon me and mock my death by making up a story! You will pay for taking the name of Herobrine in vain!

That was a very high-pitched yell.

Looks like you have a little water problem, Bonzo.

If only there were a way to dry this house out quickly...

I know! Remember the ocean monument when we dried out that room with sponges?

Of course!

I have them in my chest at home. I'll be right back.

Bring Xander with you. We need all hands on deck for this one.

We're back! Who wants a sponge?

Whatcha doin', Xander?

Looking for clues.

They've grown up so much. I hardly recognize them.

They've seen a lot of things they could never have had experienced when they were locked inside Xenos.

Do you ever miss living in Xenos?

My home is wherever you are, little sister. Xenos was a sad place for me all those years you were missing. My only happy memories are of Phoenix and Xander's family, and they're here with us now.

And I'm here thanks to them!

Hey, what's that?

Are you telling me that my little brother still believes in ghosts?

This is nowhere near the weirdest thing we've ever seen. Shulkers? Underwater temples? Zombie pigman pirates? How do you not believe what you've seen with your own eyes?

Okay, kids. Now that Bonzo's house is in shipshape, it's time to head back to bed. We won't solve this mystery tonight.

Can you guys walk Xander home? I just have one last thing to check.

Sure, Phoenix. But don't be long!

I know we left Xenos because they wouldn't accept Phoenix, but is it wrong that sometimes I think about how much safer I felt back in the village?

It's hard to be strong, Xander, especially when things get scary, but we're all here together, looking out for each other.

So what do you think it means?

The mark? Or the griefing? Or Bonzo's house?

RUSTLE

All of it. Who's behind all this Halloween mischief?

It's your first Halloween outside the protection of the village. It's only natural someone wants to take advantage and scare the pants off everyone.

I, on the other hand, have never lived in a walled village. The monks sense true disturbances and they tell us when they do. Then we investigate. We don't get scared off by silly pranks.

I'm not scared. But I have a feeling that there's something more to this story.

You've been keeping something from me, haven't you?

I...I asked the scrolls about the ghost, or whatever it was.

I thought you were going to put them away for safekeeping.

I was, but...

You said you didn't want to use them because they could be dangerous.

That's true. Sometimes knowing the truth can be dangerous. Other times, it can lead you to the answers.

And I bet this time, they just led to more questions. Since you didn't tell me right away. Or you didn't like the answer you got...

Sometimes I forget how well you know me, T.H. The scrolls did have a confusing message.

The scroll said a dark force is returning from the dead.

Of course, that doesn't necessarily mean a ghost, exactly. That's why I didn't tell Xander. But it is a mystery.

Didn't tell me what?

What are you doing here?

I thought you were trying to get rid of me, so naturally I ditched Ole Baba and Leila and hurried right back to see why.

He's here. We might as well tell him. You can't baby him forever, Phoenix.

Fine. But don't freak out, okay?

It's 2AM on Halloween night. We've just had two unexplained griefings and there's something rustling over there in the bushes. Even with all that, I'm still pretty calm...SO JUST SPILL IT ALREADY!

I asked the scrolls about what happened at the party. They kinda confirmed that some dark force is back from the dead.

He's even too surprised to say 'I told you so.'

Xander? You okay, buddy?

CHAPTER 3

What was that all about?

I think he's trying to keep the ghosts away.

KNOCK

KNOCK!

Come in!

Hey, some monk just splashed me with water.

The monks are pretty superstitious. They take ghost sightings very seriously.

Mom needs you home, Phoenix. Something happened down at Ole Baba's house.

Oh no! Is that where the scream came from last night?

I hope they're all right.

Let's go see.

Mmmmm. Coffee.

Ever since Leila returned home after being a witch for so long, she's been somewhat of a loud sleeper. She even keeps herself awake! We wear earplugs every night to drown out her snores.

Zzzzzzzz. Grnxxxxx.

It would take a lot more than a bunch of spiders to wake us up.

When we got up this morning and came downstairs, we walked into hundreds of spiderwebs.

I would have loved it when I was a witch. All those enchanted spider eyes.

At least you didn't get hurt. And you have all this string now!

But why did the griefer pick us?

Probably because we keep our door unlocked and can sleep through anything.

Actually, there's a chance it could be something more than just a griefer. Scrolls said...

You consulted the scrolls?!

We have to be careful to protect the scrolls. The fewer people who know where they are, the better.

What if someone captures you and tortures you for the information or something? You can honestly say you don't know.

I'm going to be tortured?

No one said anything about being tortured. We're fine. We've been through worse.

SPLAT!

Well, actually...

Who did you tell if you didn't tell us?

Ole Baba...I mean Bailey...knows.

You told her and not us?

Let's leave this argument for another time...Ready to ask the scroll?

Okay, Dragon Scrolls...Please tell us where the griefer will strike next.

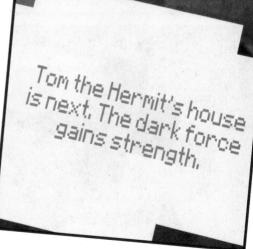

Tom the Hermit's house is next. The dark force gains strength.

Wait--it looks like there's more.

Wow. I forgot the scrolls gave you that name.

Now, you know why I've been so scared. I don't think I'm ready for this.

Xander, the Ghost Hunter, your time has come to earn your name.

Can't argue with the scrolls, little brother!

Xander, you were born ready.

So now all we need is a plan and a trap.

CHAPTER 4

TRAPPED

So, it's decided, then. A pressure plate with a lava trap underneath.

I don't know. It sounds kind of fatal for just a practical joker.

What if it's not a griefer? What if it's a real ghost? The scrolls did call me a Ghost Hunter.

What do you mean, Xander?

If it's a real ghost, the lava won't hurt him...

...or her.

And if it's a griefer, he...

...or she...

...could get seriously hurt!

Fine. A pressure plate with a water trap, then. We'll be nearby and can fish him (or her) out.

And if it's a ghost?

Probably not a ghost.

Hello: Ghost Hunter here. I wouldn't have the name if there wasn't some evil spirit lurking around waiting to be hunted.

The scrolls called you a Ghost Hunter. Not a Ghost FINDER. Whenever we set out on an adventure, we never end up finding what we think we're looking for.

You're right. When you go off looking for one thing, but you find something else that's even better, it's called serendipity. Hopefully this whole hunt will end up on a happy note.

You can think that if you want. Whatever you need to get you through this.

What do you believe?

I've worked with the monks in the monastery my whole life.

They are in tune with all the forces of the natural world. If there's a glitch or an evil force out there, they'd sense it and send my parents or me off to fix it before it becomes a problem.

Speaking of your parents, we'd better head to your house and warn them that your house is next.

They're actually not home. They're off on another business trip to build more seed worlds.

Being a pollinator is such a cool job! That's what I want to be when I grow up.

It's not enough that you're "Xander the Ghost Hunter" according to the scrolls?

WAIT! T.H., when did your parents find out about this trip?

I got a message from my dad while we were cleaning Bailey and Leila's house this morning.

Don't you think it's strange that their trip was so last minute if they're just going on a random trip to pollinate new worlds?

What are you saying?

That maybe they were called to investigate something sinister and secret...like a dark force returning from the dead.

Actually, this doesn't look too hard.
I don't think you need to be very smart to be a griefer.
But you do need to be crafty.
What about a trip wire so we can catch him or her in the act?
What does trip wire do?
Oof!
We set out a trip wire in the middle of the room. When the griefer or ghost trips, the lights go on and wake us up.
CLICK!
Pretty smart, Xander. And with all the string we collected from Bailey and Leila's house, we can set a lot of them!

I hate to say it, but being on a stakeout can be really boring.

Boring is a bad word; you're not allowed to say boring. I'm telling Mom.

Xander, come back. I'm sorry. I didn't mean boring. I meant... hungry.

Well, it is a "steak-out." Did anyone bring steak?

That's stakeout-like we wait here. Not steak like the food.

So...no steaks, then?

Zombies!

Fight quieter, Phoenix! You're gonna scare away the griefer!

I wonder why this trap didn't work.

Hmmmm...Maybe it was the redstone.

Who left the door open anyway?

Um, that was me. Sorry. I wanted some fresh air.

There, that should do it. Wish there were a way to test it without setting off the trap.

That was messy. Sorry about your house, T.H.

At least we got to test out the trip wires and the trap.

Okay, if I turn the lights back out?

We're ready. Honestly, cleaning up after a fight has to be the worst part of being a warrior.

I thought it was the smell of rotting zombie flesh.

I didn't smell bad when I was a zombie, did I?

No comment, little brother. But you smell all clean and fresh now.

Should we have kept some of that zombie flesh around to mask our scent?

Is there a small part of you that thinks our griefer may actually be a real ghost?

You don't have to answer that if you don't want to, T.H. Your beliefs are your own business.

CHAPTER 3

BAIT

Thanks for helping me fix the house up before my parents get home.

It's partially our fault it happened. We fell asleep on the job.

Since we didn't catch the griefer last night, do we have to do it again tonight?

No way. I don't think I can stand another stakeout.

Especially if there aren't any steaks.

It's clear we're not very good at stake outs.

And I'm not good at making traps.

So what do we do next?

I hate to say it, but I guess it's back to the scrolls.

Once you start checking those scrolls, it's hard to stop.

I wonder how the griefer travels at night through all the hostile mobs wandering around.

Mob heads for concealment, invisibility potion, invisibility cloak, torches...

...being a ghost...just kidding. Ghost, griefer, evil spirit...whatever it is, it's causing us to lose a lot of sleep.

Speaking of sleep, we're off to catch some zzz's.

Good idea. I'll do the same. Let me know once you hear from the all-knowning Dragon Scrolls.

Can I come with you to visit the scrolls?

You're the Ghost Hunter now...I guess you should.

Yessss!

And now for a well-earned rest.

We have to stay up all night again to trap the griefer, don't we?

This time, I think we should bring in reinforcements.

Good. I'm a growing kid! I need my sleep!

We're next but we just can't stay up all night again.

Of course we'll help you!

You poor dears. You don't need to face this alone. You should have come to us sooner.

So the scrolls said we should catch this pawn red-handed? I think I have just the thing!

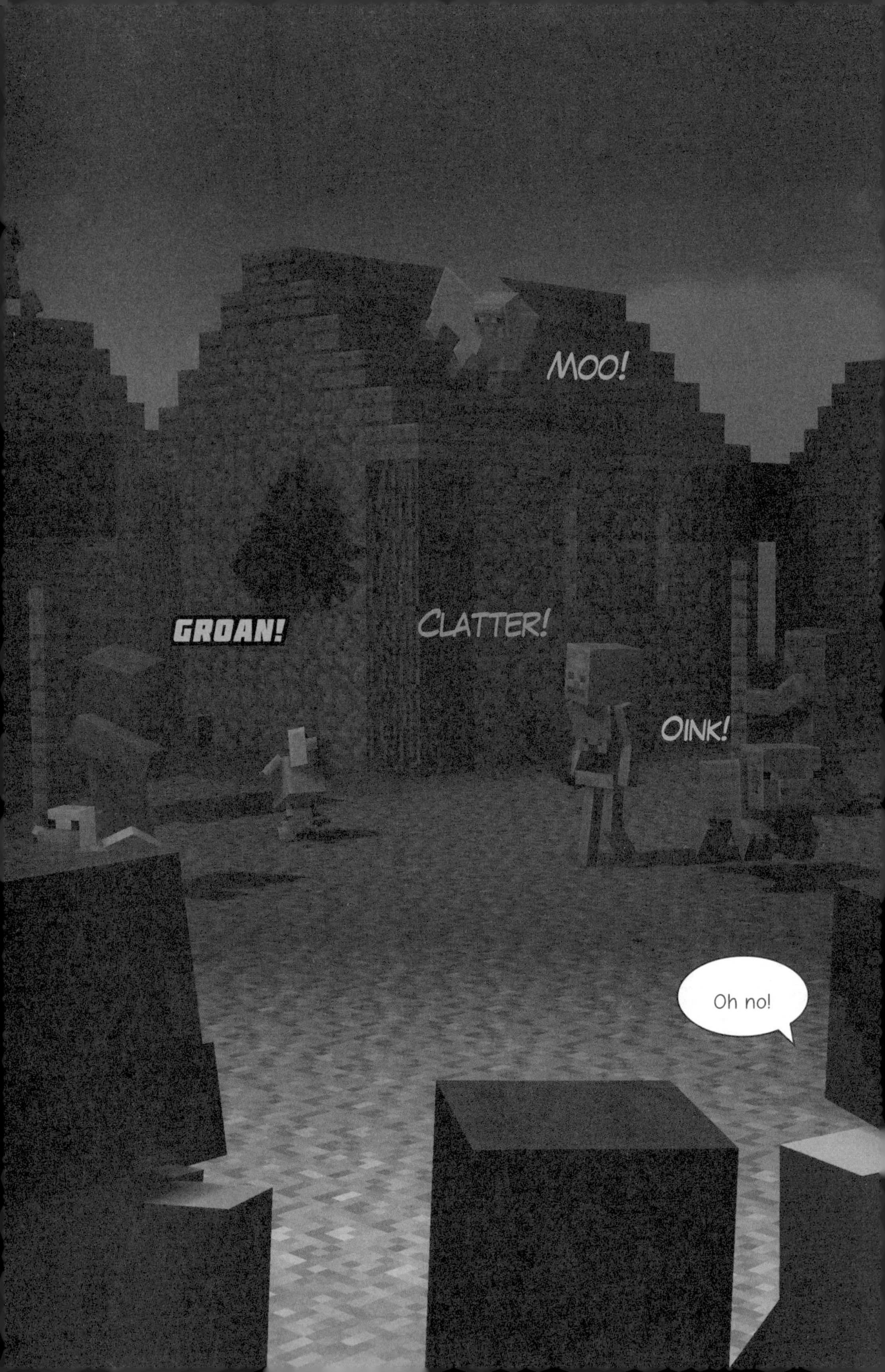
MOO!
GROAN!
CLATTER!
OINK!
Oh no!

It wasn't me--honest! I've been at your house setting a trap for Phoenix. You can go check if you want.

You've been a very busy griefer, young Kel. Is there anything else you'd like to confess?

That was quick thinking, kids!

Thank goodness you're safe. There's a wall of fire and we're cut off from the rest of the village.

Is everyone safe?

What's Kel doing here?

You know him?!

Isn't he the person you saw causing all that mischief?

No. Kel couldn't pull this off. He's just a spoiled kid with too much time and money on his hands. I knew him from the village.

I told you so.

That doesn't prove anything. Unless you saw something... Bonzo, is it?

Yeah. I saw a tall person--a grown-up--in a long black robe.

Well, we still caught you red-handed for at least one griefing. Bailey has a screenshot to prove it. But right now we need all the help we can get putting out the fire! Can we count on you?

CHAPTER 6

It looks like the fire is in good hands, so go ahead and join the rest of the kids, but watch that sword and no griefing!

I'd like to help, but I think I'm better equipped to take out those hostiles.

It was a...gift. From a friend.

Dude, that's a sweet diamond sword! Where'd you get it?

That's some gift. You must have some generous friends.

I hope you know how to use it!

Me, too.

You know, some people actually appreciate a good prank when they see it.

Is that how you got that diamond sword you don't know how to use?

Let's just say genius has its rewards.

Drink up, everyone. This will make you feel better.

A toast. To griefing bringing people together.

You faced the dragon?

Um, no. Of course not! I'm just saying diamond armor would really help.

Him? No way. Xander would probably run screaming if he saw the real Ender Dragon.

I bet you couldn't even spend a second in the Nether. You're probably a scaredy pants.

I'd never take you up on a bet like that, Kel. Going to the Nether just to win a bet is a waste of energy and resources.

I figured as much.

You're not so brave yourself. You bully people but then hide and lie about it.

You've never even used this! Kel, you could really do a lot of good for a lot of people if you switched sides to help people instead of griefing them.

Nah. It wouldn't be nearly as much fun. The looks on your faces when the lights came back on at the party... ha ha ha. Priceless!

Keldrin Arrowhead, was this your doing?

Come on, Bonzo, tell them what you saw.

No, Mom! Honest!

While these guys were catching Kel as he was about to grief Phoenix's house, I saw another griefer run by wearing a robe.

Is that what you wanted me to say?

Ugh.

Is this true? You were griefing that poor girl Phoenix and her family, while she's the reason we're free to be here in this lovely town? You owe everything to that girl and her family...

I know my Kellie wouldn't do such a terrible thing. He's a good boy.

I have a WONDERFUL idea! Let's throw a party to apologize to all of you for whatever Kel did.

They're nice children. So helpful. You should be friends with them. Play nicely.

Would you all like to come to our house tomorrow for a pool party?

A pool party? Yes please!

Um, sure. Thanks.

Yeah, I guess.

CHAPTER 7

POOL PARTY

KNOCK

GRRRFFF
SNUFFLE

I think it wants us to follow...

Grunt.

Hey! Just the people I was looking for!

Hiya, gang. Like the party? Great! Nice to see you!

Hi, Kel. Nice pool.

Thanks a lot for roping me into the cleanup crew. My parents are totally off my case now.

Oh, Kelly. Your new friends are here.

So glad you all could make it. Keldrin is really sorry, isn't he?

Oh!
Oof!
Who did that?
Oh, that Kel...he's such a trickster.
Oh, he gets it from you dear.

So, you're going to catch the guy who griefed the town, aren't you?

Well, yeah. We have to stop it from happening again.

I can help. If you need it.

You? You're the last person we'd trust.

That hurts my feelings! Besides, I'm reformed now. I've seen the error of my ways...and besides, you need me. After all, who could be better at catching a griefer than another griefer.

You've gotta admit, the slimeball does make a good point.

CHAPTER 8

THE PLOT
THICKENS

You can come back now.

So can I join you?

Fine. You can come, but you need to do exactly as we tell you.

Do I have to come, too?

Bonzo, I think it would be best if you stayed here to keep an eye on things.

Whew! That's a relief.

I mean, sure. I can do that for you.

Bring my best weapons, armor, and building supplies. Quickly.

And don't break anything this time.

Well done.

Halloween isn't over for these do-gooders. I'll give them tricks **and** treats.

The footprints stop here.

Ugh! Heavy!

Will this help?

Thanks! Wait... What? Hey! It crumbled!

Hahahaha!

Grunt!

Something doesn't feel right. This feels too easy. Like a trap.

Maybe we shouldn't go in...

Signs and supplies and plans--showing up mysteriously, suggesting things to do and people to target.

I started with Bonzo because he was the new kid.

Then the suggestions started coming in--get Ole Baba and Leila, then T.H.

Every time I pulled a prank, I got a gift.

HUMMM

CHAPTER 9

DOWN TO
THE WIRE

We have no choice. The clues lead here. Even if it is a trap, we can't be bullied. We have to solve this mystery.

Any chance Herobrine is an actual ghost and he's mad at me? Or worse, that he wants me to be his slave and keep griefing people?

It's doubtful. But if we run away, he'll just come back after us.

RATTLE!

CLACK!

SWIPE!

OOF!

Hope you don't mind but I borrowed a creeper spawn egg from your inventory.

You used it well. Quick thinking.

Here, drink this milk. You'll feel better.

Is it weird that I enjoyed the fight? It's been a while since we've had a good battle like that!

Not a bad haul from a quick battle. Who's up for some Nether cakes?

Am I the only once concerned Kel was hiding a creeper spawn egg?

These guys will love me when they find out who I am. I'm their best customer.

NETHER CAKES

It's you!

Look who just walked in, D.K.!

Hi, Scabby!

Miss Phoenix! Mr. Xander! You're back!

What's up, Chef?

I know you.

Um, maybe...I order from here a lot.

Oh! You're THAT customer.

He keeps ordering cakes and sending them back half eaten. He also keeps sending us thank-you notes that explode when we open them. He once sent us a puppy.

That was a good one, though. My delivery guys have a photo of you on the wall. See?

What are you doing hanging out with this guy?

It's a long story.

That's Kel. He's helping us catch a griefer. This is T.H.--he's our friend.

I don't know about any griefer, but did you hear Herobrine has returned?

We've heard. Believe me.

Is he here?

Yes. He has taken over a Nether fortress and set minions to guard it.

Can you show us where it is?

There it is! Just like D.K. said.
How do you know those guys anyway?
Phoenix and I rescued them when they were pirate slaves and helped them start their bakery. They were really scary at first, but they're super nice.
And great bakers!
They're much better bakers than pirates!
So you go off on adventures like this all the time? Doing good deeds? No griefing?
Yup. Whenever we get the chance.
You actually make it look fun. I might try it myself when I get back home.

CHAPTER 10

THE FORTRESS SHADOW

Are we actually going in there?
We've come this far...
CREEAAAAKKK

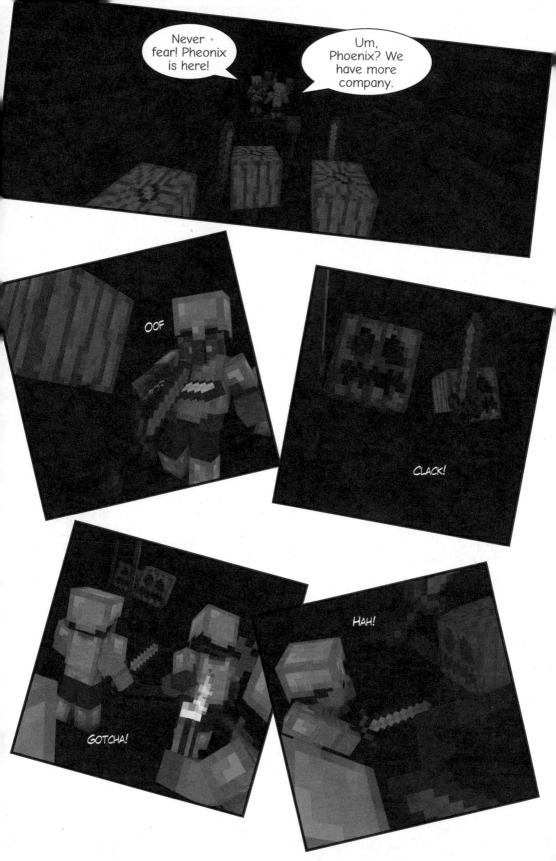

CHAPTER 11

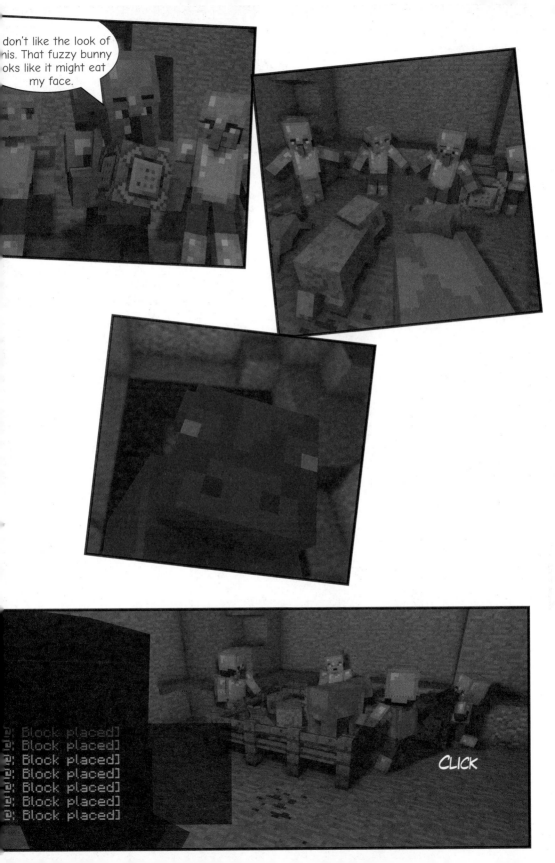

Creepers!
Why does it always
have to be creepers?
Please don't let them
explode!

RUSTLE

HISSSSSS

A minor detour. Don't worry about it, Xander.

Truce? I'm Null, by the way..

You're Null? The legendary griefer? You're the one behind all this?

You're the guy who gave me all the challenges? And the Polar Bear?

Well... kinda. I'm working for this guy...He claims to be Herobrine, but I don't know. There's something weird about him.

Weird how?

Well, this guy claiming to be the ghost came up to me and told me he admired my work. He asked me to pick out a good prankster in Phoenixtown and set out some challenges for him. Told me it would be worth my while.

I got minions and powers and an unlimited inventory of stuff...Seemed like magic to me, so I went along with it. I'd get free stuff and I'd get to learn from a master!

Until you decided to BETRAY ME!

We should have known you were behind this.
For the record, I guessed it a long time ago.

CHAPTER 12

BACK FROM THE DEAD

You can't get rid of me that easily!
Apparently not. You just keep coming back like a bad ear infection.
Uh-oh. He is so angry with me. Please protect me and I promise I'll...
Let's just return you to your family and let them decide what to do with you.

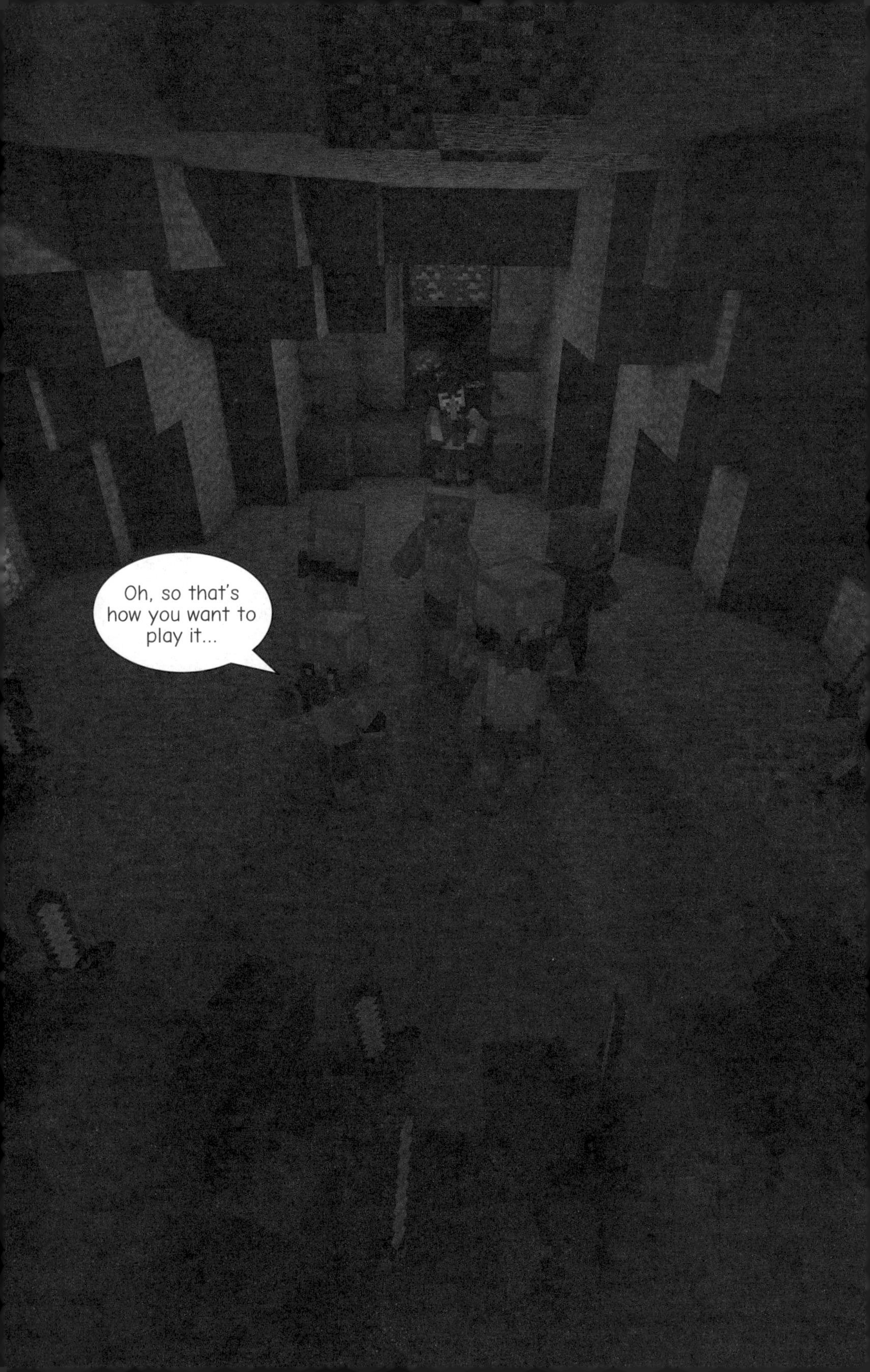
Oh, so that's how you want to play it...

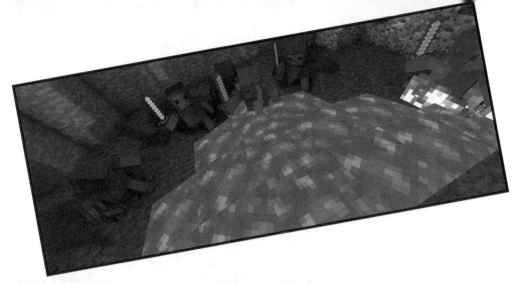

Come back here and do my bidding!

You kids are always ruining my plans!

And you're just useless.

I used it to grow stronger, summon minions, and hatch my new plan to be the one thing you children feared most...

A GHOST!

Noooooooo! Trapped by a common griefer!
I love when people under-estimate me!
[@: Block placed]
[@: Block placed]
[@: Block placed]
[@: Block placed]

Nice going, Kel!
I can't believe it but you actually did it!
You did it!
I knew I was smart to pick you. Good going.

What do we do with him now?
We'll bring him back and keep an eye on him this time.

CHAPTER 13

PARTY ON

This village is even better than Xenos now!

More fun, too!

Phoenix, Xander--have you seen Tom? We just got back and he's not home.

Tom? Oh, you mean T.H. He's out at a remote cave, guarding the Defender.

THE DEFENDER?!

Right, I forgot you left when the whole Herobrine thing went out of control...

Wasn't that just a griefer?

Kind of. Turns out the griefer, Kel, was getting ideas from another griefer, Null, who was getting the ideas from our old enemy, the Defender.

That guy just doesn't stay gone, does he?

We should have known he was behind it.

That's what we said!

You're back!

You're all right!

Hello, witch. You've changed.

I go by Leila now. My witch days are over.

I don't think this trap will hold him for long. We need a more permanent solution.

Personally, I vote for turning him into a zombie.

I vote for turning him into a witch.

I think this would be a good time to consult the scrolls.

Can you guys keep your eyes on him for a bit? Ole Baba--I mean, Bailey and I are going to figure out what to do with the Defender once and for all.

That's a great idea.

So we found the Defender, back from the dead.

I know, and you want to know what to do with him now?

Yep, so what do you recommend?

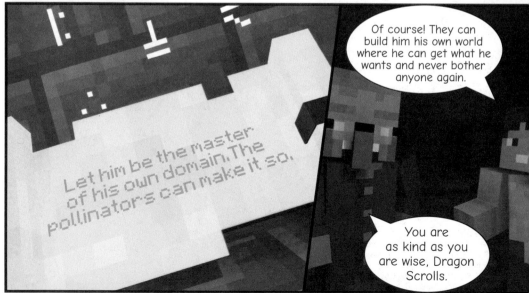

Of course! They can build him his own world where he can get what he wants and never bother anyone again.

Let him be the master of his own domain. The pollinators can make it so.

You are as kind as you are wise, Dragon Scrolls.